CONTENT

C000079519

Section A

Word Building

Q. What is Speech?
A. Spoken Words

Spoken words are composed mainly of Nouns, Verbs, Adjectives and Adverbs. These are called *parts of speech*.

Word Building is changing one part of speech to another, e.g. changing a *verb* to form a *noun*.

NOUNS
Word Building - Noun Formation

DEFINITION:

A **NOUN** is a **NAME**. It is the subject we are talking about in a sentence. It can be the name of a place, animal, person, even a feeling or an unseen thing (for example, happiness).

Look carefully at the examples below:
1) "**Susan** (person) is a good **girl** (person)."
2) "**Happiness** is getting to school on time."
In the two sentences above '**SUSAN**', '**GIRL**' and '**HAPPINESS**' are **Nouns**.

> A NOUN IS A NAME

On the next page there is a CrossWord puzzle. Before you have a go at it, look at the words listed below. Can you see how the words have changed to nouns?
For example:

WORD	NOUN
EXPLAIN	**EXPLANATION**
(what you do)	(the name of what you have done)

WORD	NOUN	WORD	NOUN
Angry	**Anger**	Sell	**Sale**
Lose	**Loss**	Sit	**Seat**
Speak	**Speech**	Proud	**Pride**
Deep	**Depth**	Live	**Life**
High	**Height**	Long	**Length**
Wise	**Wisdom**	Powerful	**Power**
Attractive	**Attraction**	Lucky	**Luck**
Choose	**Choice**	Skilful	**Skill**
Hurtful	**Hurt**	Divide	**Division**
Joyful	**Joy**	Fearful	**Fear**

Ask a member of your family to test you on the above words before you do the CrossWord.

3

NOUN CLUES

Use the clues below to complete the CrossWord - the answers are all NOUNS

ACROSS

2) Powerful (5)
3) Angry (5)
6) Wide (5)
8) Energetic (6)
12) Lucky (4)
13) Choose (6)
14) Bathe (4)
15) Hurtful (4)
18) Divide (8)
19) Speak (6)

DOWN

1) Warm (6)
2) Proud (5)
4) Fearful (4)
5) Joyful (3)
6) Wise (6)
7) High (6)
9) Skilful (5)
10) Attractive (10)
11) Live (4
12) Long (6)
16) Lose (4)
17) Sell (4)

22

Sentence Construction.
Well Done! Now think of 3 sentences using NOUNS,
Example: _Terry Bull_ **gets stuck in terrible** _traffic_ **in** _London_.

1 _____

2 _____

3 _____

Ask your parents, guardian or teacher to check your sentences to see how well you are doing.

SKIPS Challenge Time! Fun

Well Done! Now copy the letters from the coloured tiles in the CrossWord into the matching coloured boxes below to complete the sentence.

Terry Bull has a question for you:

Q) "Which word does everyone ☐☐☐☐☐ pronounce 'wrong' ?"

A) ☐☐☐☐☐ .

Enjoy!

5

MIND THE GAP, SKIP!

EXAMPLE:

Look carefully at this example of how NOUNS are used in the following sentence:

"**David** sat on a **bench** in the **park**."

'**DAVID**' is a Noun because it is a person's **name**.
'**BENCH**' is a Noun because it is an **object**.
'**PARK**' is a Noun because it is a **place**.

REMEMBER A NAME IS A NOUN

Your Challenge is to look at the lists of words below and try to fill in the gaps to match the word to the NOUN. Have Fun!

WORD	NOUN
Educate	e _ _ _ _ _ ion
Wise	w _ _ _ om
Dark	d _ _ n _ s _
Feed	fo _ _
Marry	m _ _ _ _ _ ge
Visit	vi _ _ _ _ r
Select	s _ _ _ _ _ _ on
Punish	p _ _ _ _ _ m _ _ t
Music	m _ _ _ ci _ n
Inform	I _ _ _ _ m _ _ _ on

WORD	NOUN
Beg	b _ g _ a _
Absent	a _ _ _ _ ce
Collect	c _ _ _ _ _ _ ion
Enjoy	e _ _ _ _ _ _ nt
Valuable	v _ _ _ e
Warm	w _ _ _ _ h
Assist	a _ _ _ _ _ _ n _ e
Decide	d _ c _ _ _ _ n
Brave	b _ _ _ _ _ y
Hate	h _ _ r _ d

VERBS
Word Building - Verb Formation

DEFINITION:

A **VERB** is a **DOING** word i.e. it is a word that explains what is being done or is happening.

Look carefully at the sentence below:
"The teacher **educates** the class."

In that sentence, what the teacher is **doing** is educating.
Therefore '**EDUCATES**' is the **Verb** of the noun "education".

A VERB IS A DOING WORD

On the next page there is a CrossWord puzzle. Before you have a go at it, look at the words listed below. Can you see how the words have changed to verbs?

WORD	VERB	WORD	VERB
Song	**Sing**	Growth	**Grow**
Speech	**Speak**	Sight	**See**
Soft	**Soften**	Arrival	**Arrive**
Full	**Fill**	Teacher	**Teach**
Actor	**Act**	Dark	**Darken**
Education	**Educate**	Description	**Describe**
Frozen	**Freeze**	Destruction	**Destroy**
Short	**Shorten**	Broken	**Break**
Agreement	**Agree**	Marriage	**Marry**
Sharp	**Sharpen**	Safe	**Save**

VERB CLUES

Use the clues below to complete the CrossWord - the answers are all VERBS

ACROSS

1) Song (4)
3) Speech (5)
5) Soft (6)
7) Full (4)
9) Actor (3)
10) Blood (5)
12) Departure (6)
13) Death (3)
15) Education (7)
16) Frozen (6)
18) Short (7)
19) Agreement (5)

DOWN

1) Sharp (7)
2) Growth (4)
3) Sight (3)
4) Arrival (6)
6) Teacher (5)
8) Seat (3)
11) Dark (6)
12) Description (8)
13) Destruction (7)
14) Broken (5)
17) Marriage (5)
18) Safe (4)

24

Remember a sentence always starts with a Capital letter and ends with a full stop.

Sentence Construction.
That's great! Now choose 3 VERBS to make 3 sentences,
e.g. *Kenny Dewitt* <u>ate</u> **all his vegetables.**

1 _____

2 _____

3 _____

Ask your parents, guardian or teacher to check your sentences to see how well you are doing.

www.skipscrosswords.co.uk

ANYTHING
YOU DO
IS A
VERB

SKIPS™

SKIPS Challenge Time! Trick Question

Well Done! Now copy the letters from the coloured tiles in the CrossWord into the matching coloured boxes below to complete the sentence.

Can you help *Kenny Dewitt* to answer this trick question?

Q: What ☐☐☐☐ letter word becomes *shorter* when you add

☐☐☐ letters to it?

A: ☐☐☐☐☐ .

Great! keep it up

M¹ND THE GAP, SKIP!

EXAMPLE:

Look carefully at this example of how *VERBS* are used in a sentence:

"Sally <u>watches</u> television and <u>learns</u> the names of all the stars."

'WATCHES' is a **Verb** because it is what Sally is **doing**.
'LEARNS' is also a **Verb** because it is also what Sally is **doing**.

A VERB IS A DOING WORD

Your Challenge is to look at the lists of words below and try to fill in the gaps to match the word to the VERB.

Have Fun!

WORD	VERB	WORD	VERB
Long	l _ _ _ t _ en	Success	s _ _ _ _ ed
Copied	c _ _ _	Stronger	st _ _ n _ th_ n
Division	d _ _ _ _ e	Multiplication	m _ _ _ _ _ ly
Simple	s _ _ _ l _ fy	Horror	h _ _ _ _ fy
Joy	e _ _ _ y	Terror	t _ _ _ _ fy
Ability	ab _ _	Education	e _ _ _ _ _ e
Broad	b _ _ _ _ en	Bright	br _ _ _ ten
Creator	c _ _ _ _ e	Relief	rel _ _ ve
Obedience	o _ _ y	Subtraction	su _ _ r _ _ t
Spark	s _ _ _ k _ e	Removal	r _ _ ov _

Ask a member of your family or a teacher to help you if you get stuck.

I like it

10

ADJECTIVES
Word Building - Adjective Formation

DEFINITION:

An **ADJECTIVE** is a **DESCRIBING** word, it is *the* word that describes what we are talking about in a sentence.

Look carefully at the sentence below:
"Sumira has **brown** hair."
In that sentence, we are talking about the hair that Sumira has. **'BROWN'** is the word that describes her hair, therefore it is an **Adjective**.

AN ADJECTIVE IS A DESCRIBING WORD

On the next page there is a CrossWord puzzle. Before you have a go at it look at the list of words below; they are there to help you.

Can you see how the words listed below have been changed to adjectives?

WORD	ADJECTIVE	WORD	ADJECTIVE
Sun	Sunny	Thirst	Thirsty
Week	Weekly	Music	Musical
Anger	Angry	Pride	Proud
Winter	Wintry	Noise	Noisy
Fame	Famous	Hunger	Hungry
Tallness	Tall	Ability	Able
Love	Loving	Year	Yearly
Britain	British	Boy	Boyish
Boredom	Boring	Italy	Italian
North	Northern	Length	Long

Ask a member of your family to test you on the above words before you do the CrossWord

11

ADJECTIVE CLUES

Use the clues below to complete the CrossWord - the answers are all ADJECTIVES

ACROSS

3) Week (6)
5) Ability (4)
6) North (8)
8) Pride (5)
9) Smell (6)
13) Thirst (7)
14) Tallness (4)
16) Boredom (6)
17) Boy (6)
18) Sun (5)
19) Hunger (6)

DOWN

1) Year (6)
2) Britain (7)
3) Winter (6)
4) Length (4)
5) Anger (5)
7) Music (7)
10) Love (6)
11) Fame (6)
12) Italy (7)
15) Noise (5)

21

Sentence Construction.
Now choose 3 ADJECTIVES to make 3 sentences,
e.g. *Joe King* **has a** *funny* **laugh.**

1 _____

2 _____

3 _____

Ask your parents, guardian or teacher to check your sentences to see how well you are doing.

www.skipscrosswords.co.uk

The crossword grid contains numbered cells: 1, 2, 3, 4, 5, 6, 7, 8, 9, 10, 11, 12, 13, 14, 15, 16, 17, 18, 19

**ADJECTIVE
IT TELLS YOU
SOMETHING
ABOUT THE
NOUN**

SKIPS™

SKIPS Challenge Time! Fun

Well Done! Now copy the letters from the coloured tiles in the CrossWord into the matching coloured boxes below to complete the sentence.

Joe King **wants to tell you something very important.**

"Why are Saturday and Sunday ⬜⬜⬜⬜⬜⬜ **days?"**

"Because they are not ⬜⬜⬜⬜⬜⬜⬜⬜ **."**

Great! Keep it up

13

M¹ND THE GAP, SKIP!

EXAMPLE:

Look at the example below to see how *ADJECTIVES* are used in a sentence.

"A **big** and **noisy** lorry."

'**BIG**' is an **Adjective** because it **describes** the size of the lorry.
'**NOISY**' is also an **Adjective** because it **describes** how the lorry sounds.

ADJECTIVES ARE USED TO DESCRIBE WHAT IS HAPPENING

Your Challenge is to look at the lists of words below and try to fill in the gaps to match the word to the **ADJECTIVE**. Have Fun!

WORD	ADJECTIVE	WORD	ADJECTIVE
Joy	j _ _ f _ l	Hate	h _ _ _ f _ l
Tallness	t _ _ l	Friend	f _ _ _ _ _ l _
Enjoy	e _ _ _ y _ b _ e	Attract	attr _ _ _ i _ e
Centre	c _ _ _ _ al	Strength	s _ _ _ ng
Law	l _ _ f _ l	Parent	p _ _ _ _ _ a _
Help	h _ _ _ f _ l	Man	m _ _ _ _
Health	h _ _ _ _ _ y	Force	f _ _ _ _ f _ _
Fool	f o _ l _ sh	Robot	r _ b _ _ i _
Skill	s _ _ _ f _ l	Distance	d _ _ _ a _ t
Care	c _ _ _ f _ l	Wool	w _ _ _ l _ n

ADVERBS
Word Building - Adverb Formation

DEFINITION:

An ADVERB is a word that shows how a VERB is being done or has been done.

Look carefully at the sentence below:
"Shaun walked **slowly** to the door."

In the sentence above **'SLOWLY'** is describing how Shaun walked. It is an **Adverb**.

AN ADVERB DESCRIBES AN ACTION

On the next page there is a CrossWord puzzle. Before you have a go at it look at the words listed below. Can you see how the words have changed to adverbs? It will help you to find the answers in the CrossWord.

WORD	ADVERB	WORD	ADVERB
Equal	Equally	Full	Fully
Two	Twice	Easy	Easily
Laze	Lazily	True	Truly
Joke	Jokily	Slow	Slowly
Sad	Sadly	Neat	Neatly
Soft	Softly	Calm	Calmly
Loud	Loudly	Safe	Safely
Noise	Noisily	Play	Playfully
Nice	Nicely	Most	Mostly
Short	Shortly	Friend	Friendly

15

ADVERB CLUES

Use the clues below to complete the CrossWord - the answers are all ADVERBS

ACROSS

1) Full (5)
4) Two (5)
6) Loud (6)
7) Nice (6)
9) Slow (6)
10) Most (6)
12) Mild (6)
16) Neat (6)
18) Luck (7)
19) Equal (7)
20) Play (9)

DOWN

1) Friend (8)
2) Sad (5)
3) Short (7)
5) Calm (6)
8) Easy (6)
11) Laze (6)
13) Live (6)
14) Safe (6)
15) Joke (6)
17) True (5)

ADVERBS DESCRIBE AN ACTION

21

Remember a sentence always starts with a Capital letter and ends with a full stop.

Sentence Construction.

Now choose 3 ADVERBS to make 3 sentences,
e.g. *Mick Stub* walked *carefully* across the road.

1 _____

2 _____

3 _____

Ask your parents, guardian or teacher to check your sentences to see how well you are doing.

SKIPS Challenge Time! Rearrange Letters

Well Done! Now copy the letters from the coloured tiles in the CrossWord into the matching coloured boxes below.

Mick Stub is always getting into a muddle with his letters. Can you rearrange the letters to make another word?

A) ⬜⬜⬜⬜ __ __ __ __

B) ⬜⬜⬜⬜⬜⬜ __ __ __ __ __ __

Fantastic!

17

M¹ND THE GAP, SKIP!

EXAMPLE:

Look carefully at how ADVERBS are used in the following sentence:

"Bernard thought **carefully** before he answered **slowly**."

'CAREFULLY' is an **Adverb** because it describes the way in which he thought.
(It describes the verb.)
'SLOWLY' is an also an **Adverb** because it **describes** how he answered.
(It describes another verb.)

ADVERBS DESCRIBE ACTIONS

Your Challenge is to look at the lists of words below and try to fill in the gaps to match the word to the ADVERB.
Have Fun!

WORD	ADVERB	WORD	ADVERB
Year	y _ _ _ _ y	Shy	s _ _ _ y
Day	d _ _ _ y	Pure	p _ _ _ _ y
Luck	l _ _ _ _ _ ly	Peace	p _ _ _ _ _ _ _ ly
Even	e _ _ _ _ y	Wise	w _ _ _ _ y
Close	c _ _ _ _ _ y	Fear	f _ _ _ _ _ _ _ y
Happy	h _ _ _ i _ y	Able	a _ _ y
Wild	w _ _ _ l _	Success	s _ _ _ _ _ _ f _ _ _ y
Exact	e _ _ _ t _ y	Serious	s _ _ _ _ _ _ ly
Clever	c _ _ _ _ _ _ y	Cheerful	c _ _ _ _ _ u _ ly
Care	c _ _ _ _ _ l _ y	Annual	a _ _ _ _ _ l _

Ask a member of your family to test you on the above words.

18

HOMOPHONES
Word Building - Homophone Formation

DEFINITION:

Homophones are words that sound the same as another word, **but have** different spellings and meanings.

Look carefully at the example below:
"**Our** meal took us an **hour** to prepare."

'OUR' and **'HOUR'** are **Homophones**. They **sound the same** but they are **spelt differently** and have **different meanings**.

> HOMOPHONES SOUND THE SAME, BUT ARE SPELT DIFFERENTLY

Look at the lists of words below. You will see that although they sound the same they mean different things.

WORD	HOMOPHONE	WORD	HOMOPHONE
Male	Mail	To	Two
Write	Right	Flour	Flower
Fare	Fair	Our	Hour
Plain	Plane	Reign	Rain
Sum	Some	Here	Hear
New	Knew	Blew	Blue
I	Eye	Role	Roll
Be	Bee	There	Their
Not	Knot	Sail	Sale
Bean	Been	Knight	Night

Ask a member of your family to test you on the above words before you do the CrossWord.

HOMOPHONE CLUES

Use the clues below to complete the CrossWord - the answers are all HOMOPHONES

ACROSS

1) Ate (5)
4) Knight (5)
6) Be (3)
7) Won (3)
8) Write (5)
11) Fare (4)
13) Male (4)
14) Sail (4)
16) Plain (5)
17) Stair (5)
18) Read (3)
19) Brake (5)
21) There (5)

DOWN

1) I (3)
2) Too (3)
3) New (4)
5) Our (4)
6) Blew (4)
9) Hair (4)
10) Sum (4)
11) Flour (6)
12) Role (4)
14) Sun (3)
15) Tail (4)
16) Pear (4)
18) Reign (4)
19) Bean (4)
20) Not (4)

SCRIBBLE PAD

THINK ABOUT YOUR SPELLING

28

Remember a sentence always starts with a Capital letter and ends with a full stop.

Sentence Construction.

Well Done! Now write 2 sentences using 2 HOMOPHONES in each,
e.g. *Yura Stinker* went *for* a bath at *four* o'clock.

1 _____

2 _____

Ask your parents, guardian or teacher to check your sentences to see how well you are doing.

HOMOPHONES MEAN DIFFERENT THINGS

SKIPS Challenge Time! Pronunciation

Well Done! Now copy the letters from the coloured tiles in the CrossWord into the matching coloured boxes below to complete the sentences.

Yura Stinker **wants to share a joke with you.**

1st Eskimo: "Where did your mother come from?"

2nd Eskimo: " ⬜⬜⬜⬜⬜⬜ "

1st Eskimo: "Don't bother, I'll ⬜⬜⬜ her ⬜⬜⬜⬜⬜⬜⬜ ."

Top marks

21

M¹ND THE GAP, SKIP!

EXAMPLE:

Look carefully at the example below to see how *HOMOPHONES* are used in the following sentence.

"Would you **flee** from a **flea**?"

'**FLEE**' and '**FLEA**' are **Homophones** because they **sound the same, but** they are **spelt differently** and have **different meanings.**

> HOMOPHONES SOUND THE SAME, BUT ARE SPELT DIFFERENTLY

Your Challenge is to look at the lists of words below and fill in the gaps to make **HOMOPHONES**.

Have Fun!

WORD	HOMOPHONE	WORD	HOMOPHONE
Tire	t y _ _	Flea	f _ _ e
Meter	me _ _ e	Rain	r _ _ g _
Toe	to _	Cheque	c _ _ _ k
Seen	sc _ _ e	Through	th _ _ w
Worn	w _ r _	Key	q _ _ y
Air	he _ r	Hangar	h _ _ _ e _
Bawl	b _ l _	Allowed	al _ _ d
Maid	m _ _ e	Peace	pi _ _ _
Pale	p _ _ l	Waist	w _ _ _ e
Paw	p _ o _	Wait	w _ _ _ ht

SYNONYMS
Word Building - Synonym Formation

DEFINITION:

SYNONYMS are words that have a similar meaning.

Look carefully at the examples below:
1) "Nought plus nought equals **nought**."
2) "Zero plus zero equals **zero**."
The two sentences above are similar. **'NOUGHT'** and **'ZERO'** mean similar things but are two different words, therefore we call them **Synonyms**.

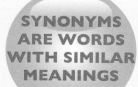

SYNONYMS ARE WORDS WITH SIMILAR MEANINGS

YOU'RE DOING REALLY WELL! On the next page is a CrossWord puzzle - the answers are all synonyms.

Go through the list, it will not only help you to understand how to use synonyms, but will also help with the answers to the CrossWord.

WORD	SYNONYM	WORD	SYNONYM
Angry	Cross	Odour	Smell
Ancient	Old	Huge	Giant
Begin	Start	Moist	Wet
Dozen	Twelve	Fall	Drop
Like	Enjoy	New	Modern
Road	Street	Protect	Guard
Lean	Thin	Hope	Wish
Zero	Nought	Circular	Round
Fast	Rapid	Attempt	Try
Speak	Talk	Foe	Enemy

www.skipscrosswords.co.uk

SYNONYM CLUES

Use the clues below to complete the CrossWord - the answers are all SYNONYMS

ACROSS

1) Separate (5)
4) Fast (5)
5) Fall (4)
6) Ancient (3)
7) Zero (6)
9) Speak (4)
11) Huge (5)
14) Jump (4)
15) Odour (5)
17) Foe (5)
18) Odd (7)
20) Moist (3)
21) Final (4)

DOWN

1) Road (6)
2) Lean (4)
3) Unhappy (3)
4) Circular (5)
6) Frequent (5)
8) Twisted (6)
10) Depart (5)
12) Question (3)
13) Dozen (6)
16) New (6)
17) Like (5)
18) Begin (5)
19) Protect (5)
20) Hope (4)

27

Remember a sentence always starts with a Capital letter and ends with a full stop.

Sentence Construction.

Now write 2 sentences using 2 SYNONYMS in each,
e.g. *Stu Pitt* **was actually** *clever* **and** *intelligent*.

1 _____

2 _____

Ask your parents, guardian or teacher to check your sentences to see how well you are doing.

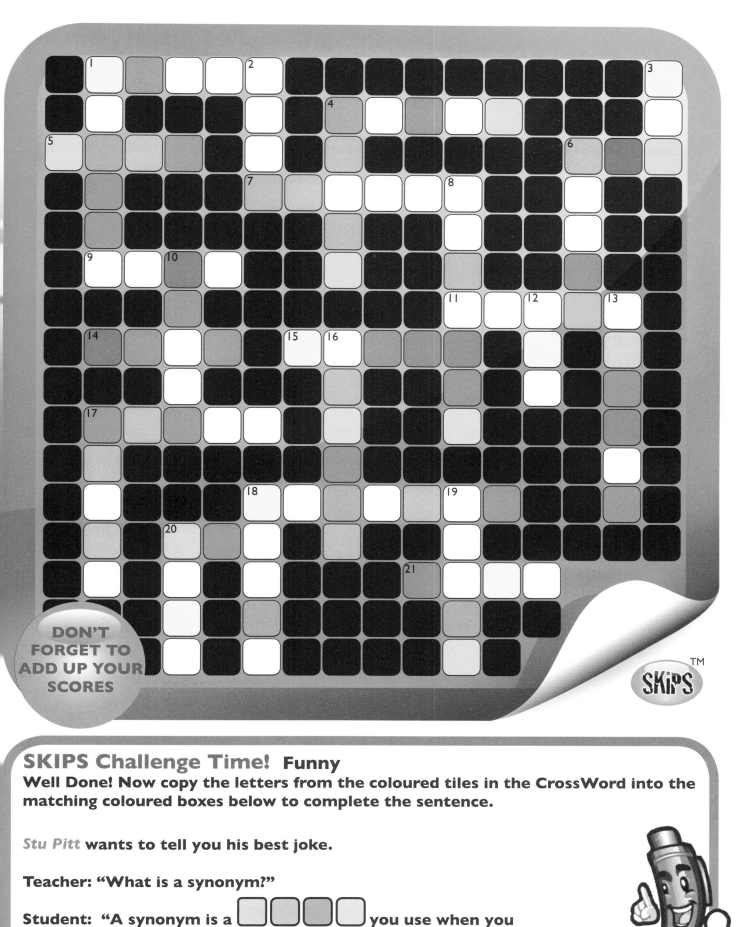

SKIPS Challenge Time! Funny

Well Done! Now copy the letters from the coloured tiles in the CrossWord into the matching coloured boxes below to complete the sentence.

Stu Pitt **wants to tell you his best joke.**

Teacher: "What is a synonym?"

Student: "A synonym is a ☐☐☐☐ **you use when you**

can't ☐☐☐☐☐ **the other** ☐☐☐ **."**

Well done!

M<u>I</u>ND THE GAP, SKIP!

EXAMPLE:

Look carefully at this example of how *SYNONYMS* are used in the following sentences.

1) "These crosswords are **<u>fun!</u>**"

2) "These crosswords are **<u>enjoyable!</u>**"

'**FUN**' and '**ENJOYABLE**' are similar in meaning to each other. We call them **Synonyms**.

SYNONYMS ARE WORDS THAT ARE SIMILAR IN MEANING

Your Challenge is to look at the lists of words below and try to fill in the missing letters to make **SYNONYMS**.

WORD	SYNONYM	WORD	SYNONYM
Difficult	h _ _ d	Halt	s _ _ p
Unhurried	s _ _ w	Interior	i _ _ _ d _
Odd	s _ _ _ n _ e	Purchase	b _ _
Thought	i _ _ a	Yearly	an _ _ _ _ l y
Ponder	t _ _ _ k	Small	l _ _ _ _ e
Exterior	o _ t _ _ _ e	Option	c _ _ _ c _
Beginner	n _ v _ c e	Conversation	t _ _ _
Guilt	r _ g _ _ t	Approve	ag _ _ _
Acute	s h _ _ p	Completed	f _ _ _ s _ _ d
Broaden	w _ _ e _	Shining	b _ _ g _ _

www.skipscrosswords.co.uk

ANTONYMS
Word Building - Antonym Formation

DEFINITION:

ANTONYMS are words that are OPPOSITE in meaning.

Look carefully at the examples below:
1) "Sven's glass was <u>**full**</u>."
2) "Sven's glass was <u>**empty**</u>."

In these two sentences we have used **'FULL'**, which means there is no more room in in the glass and **'EMPTY'**, which means that there is nothing in the glass. We call these two words **Antonyms** (*opposites*).

ANTONYMS HAVE OPPOSITE MEANINGS

Have a look at the lists of words below. Go through the list, it will help you to understand how to use antonyms before you try to do the next page.

WORD	ANTONYM	WORD	ANTONYM
Empty	**Full**	Host	**Guest**
Heavy	**Light**	Lighten	**Darken**
Hot	**Cold**	Question	**Answer**
Child	**Adult**	Accept	**Refuse**
Wake	**Asleep**	Loose	**Tight**
Dawn	**Dusk**	New	**Old**
Rich	**Poor**	Separate	**Together**
Succeed	**Fail**	Bored	**Interested**
Outside	**Inside**	Teacher	**Pupil**
Hate	**Love**	North	**South**

Ask a member of your family to test you on the above words before you do the CrossWord.

ANTONYM CLUES

Use the clues below to complete the CrossWord - the answers are all ANTONYMS

ACROSS

2) Succeed (4)
5) Outside (6)
6) Boy (4)
7) High (3)
8) Hate (4)
10) Loose (5)
15) Hard (4)
17) Accept (6)
18) Host (5)
19) Dawn (4)
20) Close (4)
22) Rich (4)
23) Run (4)
24) Question (6)

DOWN

1) Teacher (5)
2) Empty (4)
3) Heavy (5)
4) Child (5)
6) Take (4)
9) North (5)
11) Bored (10)
12) Cold (3)
13) Separate (8)
14) Awake (6)
16) Push (4)
19) Lighten (6)
20) New (3)
21) Untidy (4)

28

SCRIBBLE PAD

ANTONYMS ARE WORDS WITH OPPOSITE MEANINGS

Remember a sentence always starts with a Capital letter and ends with a full stop.

Sentence Construction.
That's great! Now write 2 sentences using 2 ANTONYMS, (opposites) in each sentence.

e.g. *Barry Schmelly* is *over* 10 but *under* 12.

1 _____

2 _____

Ask your parent, guardian or teacher to check your sentences to see how well you are doing.

www.skipscrosswords.co.uk

THINK ABOUT OPPOSITES

SKIPS™

SKIPS Challenge Time! Opposites

Well Done! Now copy the letters from the coloured tiles in the CrossWord into the matching coloured boxes below to complete the question.

Can you help *Barry Schmelly* with his opposites? *Underline* which word in the bracket is the opposite of the word made by the coloured tiles?

A) [come depart stay enter]

B) [protect attack help support]

M**I**ND THE GAP, SKIP!

EXAMPLE:

Look carefully at the examples below to see how *ANTONYMS* **are used in a sentence.**

1) "I need to **<u>divide</u>** these numbers."
2) "I need to **<u>multiply</u>** these numbers."

'**DIVIDE**' and '**MULTIPLY**' are opposites therefore they are **Antonyms**.

Your Challenge is to look at the lists of words below and see if you can fill in the missing letters to create **ANTONYMS**.

WORD	ANTONYM	WORD	ANTONYM
Exit	e _ t _ _ _ ce	None	a _ _
Hill	v _ _ l _ y	Victory	d _ _ _ _ t
Enlarge	r _ d _ _ e	Poverty	w _ _ _ th
External	i _ _ _ r _ _ l	Height	d _ _ _ h
Wild	t _ _ e	Junior	s _ n _ _ r
Future	p _ _ _	Hide	r _ _ _ al
Forgot	re _ _ _ _ _ r	Smooth	coa _ _ _
Here	t _ _ _ _	Opaque	tr _ _ _ p _ _ nt
Morning	e _ _ _ _ ng	Live	d _ _
Multiply	d _ _ _ _ e	Go	c _ _ _

www.skipscrosswords.co.uk

PAST & PRESENT

Word Building - Past and Present Tense Formation

DEFINITION:

Things that are **HAPPENING NOW** are written in the **PRESENT TENSE.** Things that have **ALREADY HAPPENED** are written in the **PAST** TENSE.

Look carefully at the examples below:
1) "Helen **goes** shopping."
2) "Helen **went** shopping."
'**GOES**' describes something that is happening now - the **PRESENT** TENSE.
'**WENT**' has already happened - the **PAST** TENSE.

Present:
"We all *fall down*"
Past:
"We all *fell down*"

On the next page there is a CrossWord puzzle. Before you have a go at it look at the list of words below; they are there to help you.

Can you see how the tenses have changed in the list below?

PRESENT	PAST		PRESENT	PAST
Sing	**Sang**		Lean	**Leant**
Come	**Came**		Choose	**Chose**
Win	**Won**		Dash	**Dashed**
See	**Saw**		Stick	**Stuck**
Wear	**Wore**		Run	**Ran**
Freeze	**Froze**		Drink	**Drunk**
Begin	**Began**		Say	**Said**
Break	**Broke**		Catch	**Caught**
Drive	**Drove**		Hold	**Held**
Feel	**Felt**		Know	**Knew**

Ask a member of your family to test you on the above words before you do the CrossWord

31

PAST & PRESENT CLUES

Use the clues below to complete the CrossWord

ACROSS

1) Past tense of begin (5)
3) Past tense of sing (4)
4) Present tense of worn (4)
5) Past tense of throw (5)
8) Past tense of come (4)
10) Past tense of freeze (5)
11) Present tense of drove (5)
12) Past tense of eat (3)
13) Past tense of fly (4)
15) Present tense of shook (5)
17) Present tense of leant (4)
20) Present tense of dashed (4)
21) Present tense of drank (5)
23) Present tense of stuck (5)
24) Present tense of won (3)

DOWN

1) Past tense of break (5)
2) Present tense of got (3)
3) Past tense of see (3)
6) Present tense of held (4)
7) Present tense of slept (5)
8) Present tense of caught (5)
9) Past tense of do (3)
10) Present tense of felt (4)
13) Present tense of fell (4)
14) Past tense of win (3)
15) Past tense of say (4)
16) Past tense of choose (5)
18) Past tense of awake (5)
19) Present tense of knew (4)
22) Past tense of run (3)

SCRIBBLE PAD

PAST HAS ALREA HAPPENEI

$\overline{30}$

Sentence Construction.
**Now choose the PAST and PRESENT tense to make 3 sentences,
e.g.** *Pu Ping* **started to** <u>*climb*</u> **the stairs and** <u>*climbed*</u> **to the top.**

1 _____

2 _____

3 _____

Ask your parents, guardian or teacher to check your sentences to see how well you are doing.

www.skipscrosswords.co.uk

PRESENT
IS HAPPENING
NOW

SKIPS™

SKIPS Challenge Time! Wise Old Saying

Well Done! Now copy the letters from the coloured tiles in the CrossWord into the matching coloured boxes below.

The great king *Pu Ping* has a favorite saying. He really wants to share it with you so you can share it with everyone you know too.

Yesterday is history, tomorrow is a mystery, but today is a ☐☐☐☐ .

That is why it is called the ☐☐☐☐☐☐☐ .

Great! Keep it up

M^IND THE GAP, SKIP!

EXAMPLE:

Look at the example below to see how the use of different tenses makes a difference to the meaning of a sentence.

"I <u>sit</u> and <u>**draw**</u>."
"I <u>sat</u> and <u>**drew**</u>."

'SIT' and 'DRAW' is the **present tense**, I am sitting and drawing **now**.
'SAT' and 'DREW' is the **past tense**, I sat and drew in the **past**.

Present:
"We all *sing* songs"
Past:
"We all *sang* songs"

Your Challenge is to look at the lists of words below and see if you can fill in the missing letters to create either the past or the present tense.

PRESENT	PAST
Become	b _ _ a _ _
Bl _ _ d	bled
Bring	br _ _ _ ht
B _ _ _ d	built
Creep	cr _ _ t
Dr _ _ _	dreamt
Fight	f _ _ _ ht
F _ _ g _ _ _	forgave
Hear	h _ _ _ d
K _ _ _ l	knelt

PRESENT	PAST
Leave	l _ _ t
L _ _ n	leant
Seek	s _ _ _ ht
S _ _ _ e	shone
Slide	s _ _ _
Steal	s _ _ _ e
T _ _ _ h	taught
Think	th _ _ _ _ t
Read	r _ _ _
Wind	w _ _ _ d

www.skipscrosswords.co.uk

In this section you need to find the correct word from the clue given below.

The clues are based on your General Knowledge.

HOW MUCH DO YOU KNOW?

Complete this page before doing the CrossWord overleaf. It will help you.

CLUES

Ten years.....D_ c _ _ e
The home of lions.....D_ _
Female horse.....M_ r _
To shout.....Y_ _ l
A male horse.....St _ l l _ _ _
Person who sells meat.....B_ _ ch _ _
A male cow.....B_ _ l
Young duck.....D_ _ k _ _ _ g
A young cow.....C_ _ f
Young lion...C _ _
The opposite of high.....L_ _
Female chicken....._ _ n
Home for bees.....H_ v _
Past tense of eat.....A_ _
Home for a cow.....B_ _ n
Opposite of difficult....._ _ _ y
The coldest season.....W_ _ _ _ r

Young sheep.....L_ _ _
Group of people.....C_ _ _ d
A male sheep.....R_ _
Group of chickens.....Br_ o _
Sound made by a horse.....N_ i _ h
A hundred years.....C_ n _ _ _ y
One who deals with crimes.....
D_ t _ _ _ iv _
Describing words.....A_ j _ _ _ _ _ es
Person who sells flowers....Fl _ r _ _ t
Where a pig lives.....S_ _
Home for a squirrel.....D_ _ y
Group of 12 things.....D_ z _ _
Where a spider lives.....W_ _
The shortest month.....F_ br _ _ _ _
Present tense of arose.....A_ _ _ e

GENERAL KNOWLEDGE

Use the clues below to complete the CrossWord

ACROSS

1) A baby sheep (4)
5) An Autumn month (9)
8) Opposite of difficult (4)
10) A male sheep (3)
12) Homophone for route (4)
13) Twelve (5)
15) Antonym for high (3)
17) Past tense of eat (3)
18) A baby cow (4)
20) Home for a squirrel (4)
22) A person who sells meat (7)
26) A hundred years (7)

DOWN

2) Describing words (10)
3) The month after March (4)
4) Sound made by a horse (5)
5) Where a pig lives (3)
6) Home for a cow (4)
7) Group of people (5)
9) A male horse (8)
11) A female horse (4)
13) Ten years (6)
14) A female relative (5)
16) A season (6)
19) Where a spider lives (3)
21) 12 months makes one of these (4)
23) A hot beverage (3)
24) A home for bees (4)
25) A type of tree (3)

SCRIBBLE PAD

DON'T FORGET TO ADD UP YOUR SCORE

28

WELL DONE!
Now you're ready to move on to the next section...

Well Done SKIP!

SKIPS Challenge Time! Trick Question

Well Done! Now copy the letters from the coloured tiles in the CrossWord into the matching coloured boxes below to complete the sentence.

Mr Luna Tick wants to see if you can answer his trick question.

Q: What does the word minimum mean?

A: A ☐☐☐☐☐ ☐☐☐☐☐☐.

Great! keep it up

Section B

English Revision

This section of the book will help you to revise what you have learnt so far. Complete the CrossWords before checking your answers to see how well you have done.

ENGLISH REVISION

Well Done so far!

The CrossWords in this section will now help you to develop your use of the English vocabulary.

Have a look at the list of words below and try to memorise them - it will really help you.

HOW MANY SIDES DOES AN OCTAGON HAVE?

FISH
Cod
Haddock
Sole
Herring
Turbot
Skate
Salmon

TREES
Ash
Oak
Elm
Cedar
Birch
Beech
Pine
Willow
Fir

METALS
Brass
Silver
Lead
Tin
Iron
Copper
Steel
Bronze
Gold

GASSES
Hydrogen
Oxygen
Nitrogen

MATERIALS
Cotton
Wool
Silk
Linen
Velvet

VEGETABLES
Cauliflower
Lettuce
Cabbage
Tomato
Potato
Carrot

BEVERAGES
Tea
Coffee
Milk
Beer
Wine
Lemonade
Juice
Coke

FLOWERS
Rose
Tulip
Daffodil
Hyacinth
Ivy
Daisy
Marigold
Buttercup

PLANETS
Mercury
Venus
Earth
Mars
Jupiter
Saturn
Uranus
Neptune

DWELLINGS
House
Palace
Hut
Mansion
Apartment
Hovel
Castle
Cottage

SHIPS
Trawler
Cruiser
Destroyer
Frigate
Yacht

FUEL
Wood
Gas
Coal

BIRDS
Eagle
Raven
Sparrow
Robin
Owl
Emu
Dove
Blackbird

SHAPES
Triangle Has 3 Sides
Quadrilateral Has 4 Sides
Pentagon Has 5 Sides
Hexagon Has 6 Sides
Heptagon Has 7 Sides
Octagon Has 8 Sides

ENGLISH REVISION 1

Use the clues below to complete the CrossWord

ACROSS

1) A month (3)
3) Doing words (5)
5) Adverb for one (4)
8) A season (6)
12) Adverb for nice (6)
13) Stationary (5)
14) Home of lions (3)
16) Homophone for four (3)
17) Remain behind (4)
19) Synonym for finish (3)
20) Homophone for reign (4)
22) Past tense of break (5)
23) Antonym for difficult (4)
24) A single thing (4)
25) Shape with 6 sides (7)

DOWN

2) Twelve months makes one of these (4)
3) Person who treats animals (3)
4) A yellow fruit (6)
6) Adjective for noise (5)
7) Present tense of ate (3)
9) A male relative (5)
10) Plural of this (5)
11) Day of the week (8)
13) Synonym for closes (5)
14) Twelve (5)
15) Winter month (8)
16) Day of the week (6)
18) Adverb for year (6)
20) To come back (6)
21) Type of tree (5)

30

SKIPS Challenge Time! Magic Numbers.

Well Done! Now copy the letters from the coloured tiles in the CrossWord into the matching coloured boxes below to complete the sentence.

No one beats *Mr Lu Zer* at Maths. Do you want to see if you can beat him in writing the answer? You can even start this question with your own number. Here we go. I bet he writes the answer before you do.

Think of any number and write it here ____. Now ☐☐☐☐☐☐ it.

Add twenty to your answer ____. Now ☐☐☐☐☐ it.

Finally take away the first number you started with ____.

Write your answer under the girl's desk on page 61 before he does.

ENGLISH REVISION 2

Use the clues below to complete the CrossWord

ACROSS

2) Female chicken (3)
5) Repair (4)
6) Adjective for wisdom (4)
8) Past tense of stand (5)
10) A single thing (4)
12) Noun for wide (5)
14) Cautious (7)
15) Adjective for year (6)
17) A dwelling (5)
20) Part of a bird (4)
22) Synonym for enemy (3)
23) Divide (8)
24) Moist (3)
25) Male duck (5)
26) To collect (6)

DOWN

1) Hinged joint between shoulder and wrist (5)
3) Homophone for knew (3)
4) Antonym for off (2)
5) Part of the face (5)
7) Adverb for slow (6)
8) Noun for see (5)
9) Homophone for deer (4)
11) A group of three (4)
13) Past tense of tear (4)
14) Young lion (3)
16) Homophone for ewe (3)
17) Antonym for home (6)
18) A female sheep (3)
19) A female horse (4)
21) A fuel (3)
24) Present tense of wore (4)

31

SKiPS™

SKIPS Challenge Time! Fun

Well Done! Now copy the letters from the coloured tiles in the CrossWord into the matching coloured boxes below to complete the sentence.

Can you help _Stan Stil_ to underline the pairs of words most similar in meaning?

Example: big, small   good, bad   <u>fast, quick</u>

A) ☐☐☐☐, story   ☐☐☐☐, small   ☐☐☐, blue

B) ☐☐☐, two   ☐☐☐, young   ☐☐☐☐☐, short

43

ENGLISH REVISION 3

Use the clues below to complete the CrossWord

YOU'RE LEARNING A LOT

ACROSS

1) A season (6)
4) Homophone for stare (5)
6) Synonym for middle (6)
7) Young goat (3)
8) Female relative (5)
10) Homophone for wear (5)
12) A married woman (4)
14) Not sharp (5)
15) Type of fish (3)
18) Mass of water covering most of the earth's surface (3)
19) Past tense of bite (3)
21) Synonym for perfect (5)
22) A season (6)
23) Antonym for last (5)
24) Hundred centimetres (5)

DOWN

1) Part of a plant (4)
2) Homophone for meter (5)
3) Antonym for odd (4)
4) Noun for speak (6)
5) Opposite of enlarge (6)
7) Past tense of know (4)
9) Land surrounded by water (6)
11) Past tense of hang (4)
12) Homophone for whether (7)
13) A month (8)
14) A woman getting married (5)
15) Young lion (3)
16) Homophone for waste (5)
17) Back of the lower leg (4)
20) Red fruit (6)

44

30

ANTONYMS HAVE OPPOSITE MEANINGS

SKIPS™

SKIPS Challenge Time! Jumbled Letters
Well Done! Now copy the letters from the coloured tiles in the CrossWord into the matching coloured boxes below. Can you help *Brook Lee* rearrange the letters to make names of vegetables?

A) ☐☐☐ ....

B) ☐☐☐☐☐☐ ....

C) ☐☐☐☐☐☐ ....

That's great

ENGLISH REVISION 4

Use the clues below to complete the CrossWord

ACROSS

1) Unhappiness (7)
4) Adult male goat (5)
6) Antonym for stand (3)
7) Past tense of use (4)
9) Antonym for bottom (3)
10) Opposite of win (4)
11) Homophone of blue (4)
12) Group of musicians (4)
15) Young lion (3)
17) Perhaps (5)
19) Present tense of drank (5)
21) Times three (6)
23) Antonym of even (3)
25) Noun of angry (5)
26) Homophone of weak (4)
27) Verb of speech (5)

DOWN

1) Past tense of sit (3)
2) Person who cares for teeth (7)
3) Day after Friday (8)
4) Little or no hair (4)
5) A colour (6)
6) Antonym of whisper (5)
8) Homophone of sail (4)
10) Baby sheep (4)
13) Straight to the point (6)
14) To place food before someone (5)
15) A fish (3)
16) Egg like shape (4)
18) Opposite of below (5)
20) A colour (3)
22) Type of flower (4)
24) Adverb for one (4)

SCRIBBLE PAD

ANTONYM
MEAN
OPPOSIT
THINGS

32

www.skipscrosswords.co.uk

SKIPS Challenge Time! Jumbled letters

Well Done! Now copy the letters from the coloured tiles in the CrossWord into the matching coloured boxes below.

Can you help *Seymour Butz* rearrange the letters to make names of zoo animals?

A) ....

B) ....

C) .... *Great fun, hey?*

ENGLISH REVISION 5

Use the clues below to complete the CrossWord

ACROSS

1) Male cow (4)
2) Homophone for plain (5)
5) Present tense of bled (5)
7) Homophone for eight (3)
8) Around (5)
12) Male relative (6)
14) Opposite of alive (4)
15) Homophone for knight (5)
18) Antonym for there (4)
19) A metal (3)
22) Male relative (3)
24) The noun for sit (4)
25) Homophone for stair (5)
27) Adjective for Britain (7)
28) Female pig (3)

DOWN

1) Very young child (4)
3) Tidy and clean (4)
4) Past tense of read (4)
6) Female dear (3)
8) Present tense of awoke (5)
9) Antonym for close (4)
10) Orange vegetable (6)
11) Antonym for ancient (6)
13) Homophone for hair (4)
16) Antonym for host (5)
17) Antonym for short (4)
20) Synonym for internal (6)
21) Present tense of taught (5)
23) Adverb for neat (6)
26) Joint between shoulder and wrist (5)

30

www.skipscrosswords.co.uk

HOMOPHONES SOUND THE SAME BUT ARE SPELT DIFFERENTLY

SKIPS Challenge Time!

Well Done! Now copy the letters from the coloured tiles in the CrossWord into the matching coloured boxes below.

Can you help *Pat Earn* underline the word that rhymes with the word in the coloured tiles?

A) ☐☐☐☐   pour   part   hurt   court

B) ☐☐☐☐☐   plait   meat   weight   pleat

Having a lot of fun?

49

ENGLISH REVISION 6

Use the clues below to complete the CrossWord

ACROSS

2) Dozen (6)
5) Angry (3)
6) Homophone for metre (5)
7) Antonym for calm (5)
8) Opposite of fresh (5)
9) Moist (3)
12) Brass wind instrument (7)
14) Number of millimetres in a centimetre (3)
17) Homophone for hire (6)
18) Antonym for married (6)
19) Homophone for write (5)
22) Past tense of dig (3)
23) Soft hair of a sheep (4)
24) A metal (5)
25) A piece of furniture (5)

DOWN

1) Opposite of west (4)
2) A hot drink (3)
3) Large flightless bird (3)
4) Noun of proud (5)
7) A five sided shape (8)
8) Extend (7)
10) Adverb for two (5)
11) A metal (3)
13) Adverb for easy (6)
15) Sound a bull makes (6)
16) Present tense of began (5)
18) Verb for song (4)
20) A building used as a home (5)
21) Homophone for wood (5)
22) Two performers singing (4)

30

www.skipscrosswords.co.uk

SKIPS Challenge Time! Jumbled Letters

Well Done! Now copy the letters from the coloured tiles in the CrossWord into the matching coloured boxes below to complete the sentence.

Can you help *Bill Ding* to rearrange the letters to make names of furniture?

A) ....

B) ....

C) .... *Think carefully!*

ENGLISH REVISION 7

Use the clues below to complete the CrossWord

ACROSS

1) Adverb of bad (5)
3) A baby sheep (4)
6) Estimate (5)
8) Opposite of tame (4)
9) Homophone for missed (4)
10) Home of a spider (3)
11) Past tense of keep (4)
12) Antonym for odd (4)
14) Relation (6)
16) Vegetable (6)
18) Opposite of stale (5)
19) Antonym for no (3)
22) Antonym of smooth (5)
24) Body part above your shoulder (4)
25) Synonym for circular (5)

DOWN

1) Male pig (4)
2) A body part (3)
4) Produced by cows (4)
5) Present tense of meant (4)
7) Verb for sharp (7)
8) Homophone for waist (5)
9) A planet (7)
10) Victory (3)
13) Antonym of full (5)
14) A fuel (4)
15) A season (6)
17) Past tense of take (4)
20) A fish (4)
21) Homophone for too (3)
23) Ancient (3)

DON'T FORGET TO ADD UP YOUR SCORES

SKIPS Challenge Time! Jumbled Letters

Well Done! Now copy the letters from the coloured tiles in the CrossWord into the matching coloured boxes below.

Can you help *Dennis Racket* rearrange the letters to make names of sports?

A) ....

B) ....

C) ....

Brilliant!

ENGLISH REVISION 8

Use the clues below to complete the CrossWord

ACROSS

1) Back of the leg, below the knee (4)
3) Adjective of heavily (5)
6) Female sheep (3)
8) Synonym for everything (3)
9) The verb for the word action (3)
10) The verb for the word full (4)
11) Homophone for sum (4)
13) A colour (5)
16) Plural of tooth (5)
18) Antonym for inhale (6)
20) Mix (5)
21) Past tense of sting (5)
22) Antonym for day (5)
23) Opposite of fast (4)
25) Past tense of mean (5)

DOWN

1) Baby cow (4)
2) Past tense of fall (4)
3) Gigantic (4)
4) A sailing boat (5)
5) Noun for warm (6)
7) Opposite of difficult (4)
12) Past tense of move (5)
13) Homophone for wait (6)
14) Opposite of external (8)
15) Large bird of prey (5)
17) Past tense of hold (4)
19) A spring month (5)
20) A yellow fruit (6)
23) Adverb for simple (6)
24) A season (6)

30

www.skipscrosswords.co.uk

SKIPS Challenge Time! Puzzle

Well Done! Now copy the letters from the coloured tiles in the CrossWord into the matching coloured boxes below and work out the following from the clues.

Ivor Problem had two goldfish, he named ▢▢▢ of them One and

the other ▢▢▢ . He did this because if One ▢▢▢▢ he'd

still have ▢▢▢ .

To continue your learning go online and see our other titles.

Section C

Answers

Well Done. Now check your answers and see how many questions you answered correctly.

Good Luck!

Page 4 NOUNS

ACROSS		DOWN	
2	Power	1	Warmth
3	Anger	2	Pride
6	Width	4	Fear
8	Energy	5	Joy
12	Luck	6	Wisdom
13	Choice	7	Height
14	Bath	9	Skill
15	Hurt	10	Attraction
18	Division	11	Life
19	Speech	12	Length
		16	Loss
		17	Sale

w r o n g s a l l y

SKIPS Challenge
Missing word: Always,
Answer: Wrong

Page 6 NOUNS

Education	Beggar
Wisdom	Absence
Darkness	Collection
Food	Enjoyment
Marriage	Value
Visitor	Warmth
Selection	Assistance
Punishment	Decision
Musician	Bravery
Information	Hatred

Page 8 VERBS

ACROSS		DOWN	
1	Sing	1	Sharpen
3	Speak	2	Grow
5	Soften	3	See
7	Fill	4	Arrive
9	Act	6	Teach
10	Bleed	8	Sit
12	Depart	11	Darken
13	Die	12	Describe
15	Educate	13	Destroy
16	Freeze	14	Break
18	Shorten	17	Marry
19	Agree	18	Save

i f v e t w o s h r

SKIPS Challenge
Missing words: Five, two
Answer: Short

Page 10 VERBS

Lengthen	Succeed
Copy	Strengthen
Divide	Multiply
Simplify	Horrify
Enjoy	Terrify
Able	Educate
Broaden	Brighten
Create	Relieve
Obey	Subtract
Sparkle	Remove

Page 12 ADJECTIVES

ACROSS		DOWN	
3	Weekly	1	Yearly
5	Able	2	British
6	Northern	3	Wintry
8	Proud	4	Long
9	Smelly	5	Angry
13	Thirsty	7	Musical
14	Tall	10	Loving
16	Boring	11	Famous
17	Boyish	12	Italian
18	Sunny	15	Noisy
19	Hungry		

s t r o n g w e e k d a y

SKIPS Challenge
Missing words: Strong,
Weekdays

Page 14 ADJECTIVES

Joyful	Hateful
Tall	Friendly
Enjoyable	Attractive
Central	Strong
Lawful	Parental
Helpful	Manly
Healthy	Forceful
Foolish	Robotic
Skilful	Distant
Careful	Woollen

Page 16 ADVERBS

ACROSS		DOWN	
1	Fully	1	Friendly
4	Twice	2	Sadly
6	Loudly	3	Shortly
7	Nicely	5	Calmly
9	Slowly	8	Easily
10	Mostly	11	Lazily
12	Mildly	13	Lively
16	Neatly	14	Safely
18	Luckily	15	Jokily
19	Equally	17	Truly
20	Playfully		

e **a** **r** **n** **s** **l** **p**

SKIPS Challenge
A) Missing word: earn
   Answer: **Near**
B) Missing word: Asleep
   Answer: **Please**

Page 18 ADVERBS

Yearly	Shyly
Daily	Purely
Luckily	Peacefully
Evenly	Wisely
Closely	Fearfully
Happily	Ably
Wildly	Successfully
Exactly	Seriously
Cleverly	Cheerfully
Carefully	Annually

Page 20 HOMOPHONES

ACROSS		DOWN	
1	Eight	1	Eye
4	Night	2	Two
6	Bee	3	Knew
7	One	5	Hour
8	Right	6	Blue
11	Fair	9	Hare
13	Mail	10	Some
14	Sale	11	Flower
16	Plane	12	Roll
17	Stare	14	Son
18	Red	15	Tale
19	Break	16	Pair
21	Their	18	Rain
		19	Been
		20	Knot

a **l** **s** **k** **m** **y** **e** **f**

SKIPS Challenge
Missing words:
Alaska, Ask, Myself

Page 22 HOMOPHONES

Tyre	Flee
Metre	Reign
Tow	Check
Scene	Threw
Warn	Quay
Heir	Hanger
Ball	Aloud
Made	Piece
Pail	Waste
Poor	Weight

Page 24 SYNONYMS

ACROSS		DOWN	
1	Split	1	Street
4	Rapid	2	Thin
5	Drop	3	Sad
6	Old	4	Round
7	Nought	6	Often
9	Talk	8	Tangled
11	Giant	10	Leave
14	Leap	12	Ask
15	Smell	13	Twelve
17	Enemy	16	Modern
18	Strange	17	Enjoy
20	Wet	18	Start
21	Last	19	Guard
		20	Wish

w **o** **r** **d** **s** **p** **e** **l** **n**

SKIPS Challenge
Missing words:
Word, Spell, One

Page 26 SYNONYMS

Hard	Stop
Slow	Inside
Strange	Buy
Idea	Annually
Think	Little
Outside	Choice
Novice	Talk
Regret	Agree
Sharp	Finished
Widen	Bright

Page 28 ANTONYM

ACROSS	DOWN
2 Fail	1 Pupil
5 Inside	2 Full
6 Girl	3 Light
7 Low	4 Adult
8 Love	6 Give
10 Tight	9 South
15 Soft	11 Interested
17 Refuse	12 Hot
18 Guest	13 Together
19 Dusk	14 Asleep
20 Open	16 Pull
22 Poor	19 Darken
23 Walk	20 Old
24 Answer	21 Neat

a r i v e d f n

SKIPS Challenge
A) Missing word: Arrive
　　Answer: Depart
B) Missing word: Defend
　　Answer: Attack

Page 30 ANTONYMS

Entrance	All
Valley	Defeat
Reduce	Wealth
Internal	Depth
Tame	Senior
Past	Reveal
Remember	Coarse
There	Transparent
Evening	Die
Divide	Come

Page 32 PAST & PRESENT

ACROSS	DOWN
1 Began	1 Broke
3 Sang	2 Get
4 Wear	3 Saw
5 Threw	6 Hold
8 Came	7 Sleep
10 Froze	8 Catch
11 Drive	9 Did
12 Ate	10 Feel
13 Flew	13 Fall
15 Shake	14 Won
17 Lean	15 Said
20 Dash	16 Chose
21 Drink	18 Awoke
23 Stick	19 Know
24 Win	22 Ran

g i f t p r e s n

SKIPS Challenge
Missing words:
Gift, Present

Page 34 PAST & PRESENT

Became	Left
Bleed	Lean
Brought	Sought
Build	Shine
Crept	Slid
Dream	Stole
Fought	Teach
Forgive	Thought
Heard	Read
Kneel	Wound

Page 35 GENERAL KNOWLEDGE

Decade	Lamb
Den	Crowd
Mare	Ram
Yell	Brood
Stallion	Neigh
Butcher	Century
Bull	Detective
Duckling	Adjectives
Calf	Florist
Cub	Sty
Low	Drey
Hen	Dozen
Hive	Web
Ate	February
Barn	Arise
Easy	
Winter	

Page 36 General Knowledge

ACROSS	DOWN
1 Lamb	2 Adjectives
5 September	3 April
8 Easy	4 Neigh
10 Ram	5 Sty
12 Root	6 Barn
13 Dozen	7 Crowd
15 Low	9 Stallion
17 Ate	11 Mare
18 Calf	13 Decade
20 Drey	14 Niece
22 Butcher	16 Winter
26 Century	19 Web
	21 Year
	23 Tea
	24 Hive
	25 Fir

s m a l o t h e r

SKIPS Challenge
Answer: Small Mother

Page 40 ENGLISH 1

ACROSS
1 May
3 Verbs
5 Once
8 Autumn
12 Nicely
13 Still
14 Den
16 For
17 Stay
19 End
20 Rain
22 Broke
23 Easy
24 Unit
25 Hexagon

DOWN
2 Year
3 Vet
4 Banana
6 Noisy
7 Eat
9 Uncle
10 These
11 Thursday
13 Shuts
14 Dozen
15 November
16 Friday
18 Yearly
20 Return
21 Beech

d
o
u
b
l
e
h
a
v

SKIPS Challenge
Missing words:
Double, halve
Answer: 10
(Did Mr Lu Zer beat you?)

Page 42 ENGLISH 2

ACROSS
2 Hen
5 Mend
6 Wise
8 Stood
10 Unit
12 Width
14 Careful
15 Yearly
17 Abode
20 Wing
22 Foe
23 Separate
24 Wet
25 Drake
26 Gather

DOWN
1 Elbow
3 New
4 On
5 Mouth
7 Slowly
8 Sight
9 Dear
11 Trio
13 Tore
14 Cub
16 You
17 Abroad
18 Ewe
19 Mare
21 Gas
24 Wear

t
e
l
i
n
y
r
d
o
f
b

SKIPS Challenge
A) Missing words:
Tell, tiny, red
Answer: Tiny Small
B) Missing words:
One, old, brief,
Answer: Brief Short

Page 44 ENGLISH 3

ACROSS
1 Summer
4 Stair
6 Centre
7 Kid
8 Niece
10 Where
12 Wife
14 Blunt
15 Cod
18 Sea
19 Bit
21 Ideal
22 Autumn
23 First
24 Metre

DOWN
1 Stem
2 Metre
3 Even
4 Speech
5 Reduce
7 Knew
9 Island
11 Hung
12 Weather
13 February
14 Bride
15 Cub
16 Waist
17 Calf
20 Tomato

a
e
p
o
t
c
r

SKIPS Challenge
Answers:
A) Pea
B) Potato
C) Carrot

Page 46 ENGLISH 4

ACROSS
1 Sadness
4 Billy
6 Sit
7 Used
9 Top
10 Lose
11 Blew
12 Band
15 Cub
17 Maybe
19 Drink
21 Treble
23 Odd
25 Anger
26 Week
27 Speak

DOWN
1 Sat
2 Dentist
3 Saturday
4 Bald
5 Yellow
6 Shout
8 Sale
10 Lamb
13 Direct
14 Serve
15 Cod
16 Oval
18 Above
20 Red
22 Rose
24 Once

l
i
o
n
m
k
e
y
c
a

SKIPS Challenge
Answers:
A) Lion
B) Monkey
C) Camel

Page 48 ENGLISH 5

ACROSS
1 Bull
2 Plane
5 Bleed
7 Ate
8 About
12 Nephew
14 Dead
15 Night
18 Here
19 Tin
22 Son
24 Seat
25 Stare
27 British
28 Sow

DOWN
1 Baby
3 Neat
4 Read
6 Doe
8 Awake
9 Open
10 Carrot
11 Modern
13 Hare
16 Guest
17 Tall
20 Inside
21 Teach
23 Neatly
26 Elbow

p
o
r
t
l
a
e

SKIPS Challenge
A) Missing word: Port
Answer: Court
B) Missing word:
Plate
Answer: Weight

Page 50 ENGLISH 6

ACROSS
2 Twelve
5 Mad
6 Meter
7 Panic
8 Stale
9 Wet
12 Trumpet
14 Ten
17 Higher
18 Single
19 Right
22 Dug
23 Wool
24 Steel
25 Table

DOWN
1 East
2 Tea
3 Emu
4 Pride
7 Pentagon
8 Stretch
10 Twice
11 Tin
13 Easily
15 Bellow
16 Begin
18 Sing
20 House
21 Would
22 Duet

t
a
b
l
e
c
h
i
r
s

SKIPS Challenge
Answers:
A) Table
B) Chair
c) Settee

ACROSS	DOWN
1 Badly	1 Boar
3 Lamb	2 Leg
6 Guess	4 Milk
8 Wild	5 Mean
9 Mist	7 Sharpen
10 Web	8 Waste
11 Kept	9 Mercury
12 Even	10 Win
14 Cousin	13 Empty
16 Potato	14 Coal
18 Fresh	15 Spring
19 Yes	17 Took
22 Rough	20 Sole
24 Neck	21 Two
25 Round	23 Old

ACROSS	DOWN
1 Calf	1 Calf
3 Heavy	2 Fell
6 Ewe	3 Huge
8 All	4 Yacht
9 Act	5 Warmth
10 Fill	7 Easy
11 Some	12 Moved
13 White	13 Weight
16 Teeth	14 Internal
18 Exhale	15 Eagle
20 Blend	17 Held
21 Stung	19 April
22 Night	20 banana
23 Slow	23 Simply
25 Meant	24 Winter

SKIPS Challenge
Answers:
A) Rugby
B) Cricket
C) Hockey

SKIPS Challenge
Missing words:
One, Two, died, Two

SCRIBBLE PAD:

SCRIBBLE PAD:

ORDER FORM

	TITLE		RRP
	SKIPS KS1 CrossWord Puzzles Key Stage 1 English	ISBN 978-0-9567526-5-9	£7.99
	SKIPS KS1 CrossMaths Puzzles Key Stage 1 Maths	ISBN 978-0-9567526-4-2	£7.99
	SKIPS KS2 CrossWord Puzzles Key Stage 2 English Book 1	ISBN 978-0-9567526-6-6	£7.99
	SKIPS KS2 CrossWord Puzzles Key Stage 2 English Book 2	ISBN 978-0-9567526-2-8	£7.99
	SKIPS KS2 CrossMaths Puzzles Key Stage 2 Maths Book 1	ISBN 978-0-9567526-7-3	£7.99
	SKIPS KS2 CrossMaths Puzzles Key Stage 2 Maths Book 2	ISBN 978-0-9567526-3-5	£7.99
	SKIPS 11+ CrossWord Puzzles 11 Plus English	ISBN 978-0-9567526-0-4	£9.99
	SKIPS 11+ CrossMaths Puzzles 11 Plus Maths	ISBN 978-0-9567526-1-1	£9.99

Teachers and Tutors

You will be eligible for discounts on purchases of sets of 10 copies or more. Please get in touch for more details.

 sales@skipscrosswords.co.uk

 www.skipscrosswords.co.uk

SKIPS Crosswords
142 Newton Road, Great Barr
Birmingham B43 6BT
United Kingdom

For more SKIPS titles visit our website.